Wee Peter Puffin

Wee Peter Puffin

by
Jane Weinberger

A WINDSWEPT BOOK

Windswept House • Mt. Desert, Maine

Design and Illustrations
by Alek Kardas

Copyright ©
by Jane Weinberger 1984

Library of Congress
Catalogue Number 84–051 988

ISBN 0-932433-03-0

Printed in the
United States of America

Permission to use the poem "There once was a Puffin"
by Florence Page Jaques has been granted by The Nature
Conservancy of Arlington, Virginia. The poem is from
Child Life, copyright 1930, 1953 Rand McNally.

Map courtesy of
DeLorme Mapping Company
Freeport, Maine

15   14   13

For
Becky and James

Other Stories
by Jane Weinberger

Sarah and Fanny

Vim, A Very Important Mouse

That's What Counts

Tabetha Jones

Plympton - Series

You will perhaps remember
the nursery rhyme that reads:

"There once was a Puffin,

Just the shape of a Muffin,

Who lived on an Island in the

deep blue sea.

He ate little Fishes,

Which were most delicious,

He had them for breakfast and

he had them for tea."

That was not Peter Puffin although Peter does live on an island. He lives on Matinicus Rock off the Coast of Maine which most certainly is an island and it is in the deep blue sea.

Peter is an only child. He has no brothers or sisters. He does have a few friends who live in burrows tunneled into the rocky ledge. He was born on Matinicus Rock and comes back there most every Spring.

One day Peter and his very special friend, Patti Puffin, went to play on the shore. They pattered along the beach, jumping over rocks and catching little

fish. And they decided that
when they were old enough
they would become mates
and have a baby puffin of
their own.

Shortly after that all the puffins went back to live in the water, each to his own favorite place. For many months Peter Puffin lived on the sea. He tossed about on the wildest waves. He even slept on the water, just tucked his head under his wing and went sound asleep. When he was hungry he dove into the ocean for fish. And on sunny afternoons he just floated along. Most of the time he was all alone. He liked to be alone.

But one lovely Spring
morning he woke up with
a strong desire to go home
to his Island. He wanted
to see the other puffins.
After all, he had been
away for a very long time.
So he headed straight
home for Matinicus Rock
and he did not get lost on
the way.

When he arrived he found that a great many of
his friends had come, too. In fact there were so man
puffins there that at first he did not see Patti. She sa
him and recognized him at once, although he had hi
new colors on. His bill was bright red touched with

bit of blue and had a gold rim and he had a bright
yellow rose on each side of his mouth. He looked like
a little clown with his eyes circled in red with a
triangle of blue above and below. His feet were also
painted red.

Patti, too, was wearing her brilliant Spring colors and they soon found each other. For several days they played together and they mated there on the waters off Matinicus Rock. She was his wife and he was her husband. They were very happy.

They found their old burrow, but there was a rabbit in it. He had thought it was not anyone's house so he had moved into it and he was there to stay.

Peter and Patti found another burrow and made their nest in that.

In May Patti laid a lovely large white egg with pretty lilac-colored trimmings on it. She and Peter took turns covering it with their wings

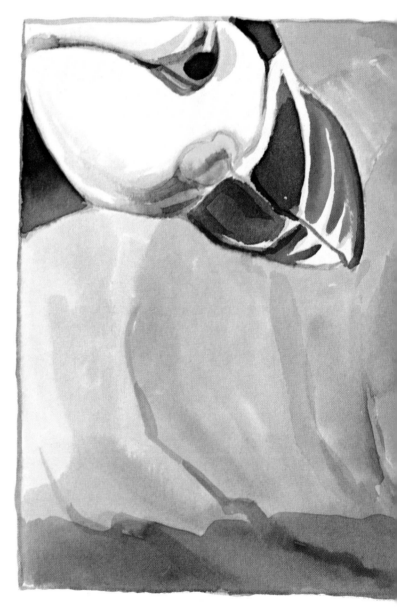

ecause their little baby puffin was
rowing inside the egg and had to be
ept warm.

One day in June—it was June 10th, I think—Patti heard sounds coming from the egg. It was their little one trying to sing. She and Peter listened and cooed softly back to the baby puffin. Soon the shell was pecked

pen and the baby puffin emerged. He was
ike a small fluffy ball and was called Wee
Peter. He was always hungry. He kept Peter
nd Patti busy bringing little fishes to feed
im.

One day when Patti was
flying back to him with her
beak full of fishes, a naughty
seagull darted at her and
made her drop the little
fishes. Then he ate them
all himself. Seagulls cause
puffins a lot of trouble.

Never mind. Peter had more fish for Wee Peter. In fact, Patti and Peter have fed that baby more than a thousand fish and now Wee Peter is nearly as large as his father.

He is grown up
enough to take care of
himself. Peter and Patti
can go back to living
on the sea without him.

Wee Peter stayed on in the nest for a short while. Then he too decided to leave. One night he walked down to the edge of the cliff and jumped into the sea. Just like that. He liked the water and he swam off into the Atlantic Ocean as all good puffins do.

I think he will come back to Matinicus Rock, don't you?

There Once Was a Puffin

Oh, there once was a Puffin
Just the shape of a muffin,
And he lived on an island
In the
        bright
            blue sea!

He ate little fishes,
That were most delicious,
And he had them for supper
And he
       had
          them
             for tea.

But this poor little Puffin,
He couldn't play nothin',
For he hadn't anybody
To
      play
         with
            at all.

So he sat on his island,
And he cried for awhile, and
He felt very lonely,
And he
          felt
                    very small.

Then along came the fishes,
And they said, "If you wishes,
You can have us for playmates,
Instead
          of
                    for
                              tea!"

So they now play together,
In all sorts of weather,
And the Puffin eats pancakes,
Like you
          and
                    like
                              me.

Florence Page Jaques

Wee Peter Puffin

Words by Florence Page Jaques
Music by Jeanne Cleaves Fernald

Brightly!

Oh -- there once was a Puf-fin in the shape of a muf-fin, and he lived on an Is-land in the deep blue sea. He ate lit-tle fish-es that were most de-li-cious and he had them for sup-per and he had them for tea. But this poor puf-fin he couldn't play noth-in' For he had-n't an-y bo-dy to play with at all So he sat on his is-land and he cried for a-while and he felt lone-ly and he felt ver-y small. Then a-long came the fish-es and they said, "If you wish-es you can have us for play-mates In-stead of for tea. So they now play to-geth-er in all sorts of weath-er, and the Puf-fin eats pan-cakes like you and like me!

Much slower tempo

Tempo I